MORAL STORIES OF
GRANDPA

This
Book belongs
to ...

....

....

....

MORAL STORIES OF
GRANDPA

ALKA'S BOOK
An imprint of ALKA Publications
2005 © **Alka Publications Mumbai**

❀ Retold by ❀
Rashmi Jaiswal

❀ Illustrated By ❀
P. P. Kasbekar

❀ Processed by ❀
Meta Process

❀ Printed by ❀
Shreeji Creations

Published by :
ALKA PUBLICATIONS
2 Sai Sadan, 76 / 78, Mody Street, Fort, Mumbai - 400 001. India
Tel. : 2262 4439 / Tel. Fax : 2263 2585
Website : www.alkapublications.com • E-mail :
manojlakhani@vsnl.net

Index

The Sour Grapes

A hungry fox was walking through a vineyard. The big ripe bunches of grapes tempted the fox.

"What fine looking grapes these are! These will certainly satisfy my hunger," thought the fox.

However, the grapes were beyond his reach. The fox stretched his neck and tried to hold the bunch of grapes in his mouth. The grapes were still far above.

So, the fox stood on his hind legs and stretched himself to catch the grapes with his fore legs. Alas! The fox could not touch the grapes even then.

The fox jumped and jumped for a long time to get hold the bunch of grapes, but failed every time.

At last disappointed by his efforts, the tired fox

said to himself, "These grapes are sour. Who would like to eat these sour grapes?" Saying this, the fox left the vineyard.

What we do not get is declared worthless by us.

Hunting with a Lion

Once a wolf, a bear and a jackal went hunting under the leadership of a lion. On way, they came across a buffalo. The four of them cordoned off the buffalo and killed him with their joint efforts. The body of the buffalo was cut into four parts.

All of them were eager to eat their share.

Suddenly the lion, their mightiest partner roared, "Wait! If anyone is eager to have his part of prey, then listen to me first! Being the partner of this hunting team, I should get the first part of the buffalo. Being the leader of our hunting team, I must get the second part. I want the third part of it for my cubs. And if anyone of you is willing to claim the fourth part, he should come and fight with me to get it."

Hearing this, the three poor fellows walked away quietly leaving all the parts of the spoil for the lion.

It's not wise to have a partnership with mightier.

The Wolf and the Crane

O ne day a hungry wolf found a big dead animal. He at once jumped upon it and began eating hurriedly. The wolf was in such a haste that while eating, a bone got stuck in his throat. The wolf tried hard to bring the bone out, but failed miserably. The greedy wolf even tried to swallow the bone to continue eating, but didn't succeed.

At last, he went to a crane that lived by the river. The wolf said to the crane, "A bone has got stuck in my throat while eating. Please extract it out with the help of your long neck and beak. You will be well paid

for this obligation."

The crane agreed. He inserted his long beak inside the wide-open mouth of the wolf. The crane's long neck helped him in reaching down the throat and pulling the bone out.

After accomplishing the work successfully, the crane said, "Now pay for my service!"

The cunning wolf laughed, "Ha, Ha, Ha! Payment for your service! You thank me for allowing you to bring out your head safely from my mouth."

Never believe a wicked person's promise.

The Sky is Falling

A strong wind was blowing. It was making mysterious whistle sounds in the forest. A timid rabbit was very much frightened with the whole atmosphere. He hid himself in his burrow under the mango tree.

Suddenly, he heard a heavy thud sound. The frightened rabbit sprang out of his burrow and ran through the forest. The rabbit was shouting loudly, "Run, sky is falling!"

On the way, the jackal saw the scared rabbit running. He asked, "What happened, why are you running in such haste?" "Didn't you hear the loud heavy sound? The sky is falling. Run for your life," replied the rabbit while running.

The jackal too started running with him. On the way, they met a giraffe. The giraffe enquired why they were running helter-skelter. And when he came to know that the sky was falling, he joined them too. Soon the elephant, the deer, the horse all joined the running group.

Hearing the din, the lion came out of his den and asked, "Why are you making so much of fuss?"

The animals replied in chorus, "The sky is falling down and we are running to save our lives".

The lion was very much surprised to hear this unique statement. He asked, "How did you know this?" "I saw a piece of sky falling down with a big 'thud' sound," replied the rabbit quite excited.

The lion was skeptical about what the rabbit had to say. So he said, "Can you show me the place where the piece of sky has fallen down?"

Though the rabbit was scared, he led the lion and the other animals to the mango tree where he had heard the sound.

There, the lion saw a big mango lying. He picked up the mango and said, "So, this is the piece of sky!"

The animals were ashamed when they realized that they ran like fools on hearsay.

> **Do not jump on any conclusion**
> **before investigating the matter fully.**

The Peepal and the Reeds

On the bank of a river, there was a tall and sturdy peepal tree. Near that peepal tree, some reeds had grown on the ground. The reeds were weak and slender. Whereas the peepal tree looked huge and sturdy.

The tree was very much proud of its size and strength. He often ridiculed the weak reeds. One day the peepal tree boasted, "Look, how strong I am! I can resist the powerful wind without bowing down before it. But you reeds are so weak that you can not even sustain the soft breeze and start trembling with fear."

The tree continued with his boastful talk, "I'm so strong that I can block the way of the wind, whereas you weak vegetations bow down even before the gentle blow of the wind."

After hearing such talk from the peepal tree, the reeds said humbly, "Of course we are weak in front of the strong wind and so we pay our respect to the wind by bowing down in front of it. I think that you should also sometimes bow down in front of the powerful wind."

The arrogant tree laughed aloud, "Ha, Ha! I am not a reed who bows down to all and everyone. I'm a stout peepul tree who never bends."

The wind, which had been listening to the tree's arrogant talk for a while, couldn't tolerate it anymore.

It blew so hard that the tall and sturdy peepal tree was uprooted and thrown on the ground. However the weak and slender reeds survived because they bowed to save themselves from the strong wind's blow.

Humility always conquers pride.

The Sparrows and the Farmer

A mother sparrow had built a nest amidst the crops of the field. She lived there with her two newborn babies. The little sparrows were happy in their nest.

Slowly, they grew up and learnt flying. Time passed and then came the harvest season. The little sparrows keenly observed the harvest taking place in the other fields. They said to their mother, "Mom, now we should fly away from here. The farmer of this field will also be coming for reaping his crops."

The mother replied, "The farmer is not ready. We

needn't fly so early."

After a few days, the farmer came into the field with his neighbour. He discussed the harvest and requested him to come the following day to help him in the harvest.

The baby sparrows again asked, "Mom, should we fly now?" The mother replied, "No my dear, the neighbour will not turn up tomorrow in this busy harvest season. There is no need to fly."

Next day, the farmer came to his field. He said to himself, "Nothing to worry. If my neighbour has not come, I'll call my relatives for help."

The babies were anxious. They again asked their mother whether it was the right time to fly.

But the experienced mother told them to be patient.

A few days later, the farmer came to the farm alone with a sickle in his hand. The mother sparrow said to her children, "Come on my children! Let's fly from this field. Today, the farmer has decided to harvest the crop himself."

Self-dependence brings certainty.

Belling the Cat

O nce upon a time, there lived many mice in a grocer's shop. The mice created menace in the shop. Not a single food item of the shop remained untouched by these mice. They had enough to eat and spoil in the shop.

The mice had a gala time with the foodstuff like bread, biscuits, grains and other eatables. The owner of the shop was upset with the heavy loss he was incurring.

One day, the grocer thought of an idea and bought a big agile cat. Soon the cat ate up a few of the mice. The mice were frightened. Their free movement in the shop was restricted. Their life did not remain pleasant any more. A few of them were being caught by the cat everyday.

So the troubled mice held an urgent meeting to find a solution to their problem. In the meeting,

everyone agreed that in order to live peacefully they had to get rid of the cat.

A mouse said, "If somehow we could know when the cat comes towards us, we can hide ourselves to safety well in time."

Another young mouse suggested, "How nice it would be if a bell could be tied around the cat's neck! Whenever the cat moves, the bell will ring and we will know that the cat is somewhere nearby."

All the mice rejoiced on hearing this wonderful suggestion. They clapped their hands in joy and praised the young mouse.

Amidst the cheer of happiness, an old mouse stood up and said, "Wait! Before cheering, you must decide who is going to bell the cat?"

Silence prevailed all over. No one came forward with the reply.

Imaginary solutions never serve a purpose.

Friendship of the Owl and the Swan

In a dense forest, there was a beautiful lake. In this lake, there lived a swan.

One day an owl came there. The owl liked the ambience around the lake and started living there. The swan also liked the company of the owl and very soon they became good friends.

Months passed. One day the owl said, "O dear friend! It's been long since I left my home. Now I want

to go back to my nest. My nest is on a big banyan tree near the river. I invite you to visit my place." The owl then said goodbye and flew away.

After some time, the swan decided to visit the owl's place and flew towards the banyan tree.

When the swan reached there, it was daytime. As the owl could not see in the broad daylight, the swan waited for the evening to arrive.

Since the swan was quite tired after a long journey, he went to sleep in the owl's nest.

When the sun set and darkness spread all around, the owl could see clearly. But the swan was sleeping then. That night, a few travellers took shelter under

the banyan tree. With the dawn break, they were ready to continue further on their journey. When the travellers were about to begin their journey the owl started hooting.

The hooting of an owl was considered a bad omen. Irritated by the owl's hooting, the travellers took out there bows and arrows and shot at the owl. It was still dark and the owl could see the travellers targeting at him. He swiftly flew away from the tree. The poor swan, who was sleeping in the owl's nest, became the target of the arrows and died immediately.

One should make friends with their own kind.

The Clever Prince

Princess Bhanumati of Nayagad was a beautiful young maiden. A number of princes from different kingdoms wanted to marry her. A contest was organized to select the right match for the princess. The princess made a unique announcement, "I will marry the prince who forces me to break my silence".

Several princes came to Nayagad and accepted the challenge. They sat before the princess and through various actions they tried to make her laugh or speak, but in vain. All of them failed miserably and returned to their respective kingdoms.

One day, an old man came to Nayagad. He introduced himself as the prince of Sundernagar. He said to the king, "I've heard that the princess has thrown a challenge on the princes who are willing to

marry her. I've come here to accept the challenge and would like to try and break her silence."

As per the announcement, the contestant should be a prince and the old man was fulfilling the requirement. Therefore, the king allowed him to participate in the contest. Princess Bhanumati came in the court and sat before the old prince for the contest.

As soon as she sat, the old prince got up from his seat and swiftly moved up to her. He held her hand tightly and said in a very emotional voice, "O dear, I know you were waiting for me since long. We love each other so much that now we cannot stay away. Why don't you tell your parents about our love?"

Shocked by his sudden approach and display of love, the princess forgot that she did not have to speak.

She shouted angrily, "Who are you? You liar! I have never loved you. Why should I love an old man like you?"

Hearing this, the prince laughed and removed his wig and make up. A handsome prince was standing before her.

Everyone was surprised to see the handsome prince. The princess happily accepted her defeat and married with the clever prince.

Fate favours the brave.

The Lion and the Mouse

One day after his lunch, the king lion was taking a nap under a shady tree. Near the tree, there was a hole where lived a little mouse. The mouse was naughty. He came out of the hole and saw the lion sleeping. Just to have some fun, the mouse climbed up on the huge body of the lion and then climbed down running.

The young mouse found it very interesting. He repeated his actions again and again. The mouse's movement tickled the lion's body. He woke up and found the mouse running over his body. He caught the mouse in his paw and said angrily, "You fool, you

are playing on a lion's body! You'll be surely killed by me."

The mouse was frightened. He begged, "Please forgive me! I'll never do this again. Please grant my life, and I'll repay you for your kindness in the future!"

The lion laughed at the mouse's remarks. He said, "You small creature! How can you be of any help to a mighty lion like me?"

However, the lion felt pity and allowed the mouse to go.

A few days later when the mouse was inside his hole, he heard the angry roar of the lion. The mouse peeped out and saw a lion in the hunter's trap.

The mighty lion was helpless and was trying hard

to come out of the net. The little mouse remembered the kindness of the lion and rushed to help him. He swiftly nibbled the net and freed the lion.

Help can be got from unexpected quarters.

The Neem Tree and the Travellers

One hot summer afternoon, two travellers were passing through a dusty village road.

It was the harvest time, so the village fields gave a dry deserted look. The travellers were tired of walking so long. They wanted to relax somewhere. However, as long as they could see there was no tree visible, where they could relax.

Unable to find any resort, they kept walking in the bright sun. After sometime, they saw a lush green shady neem tree. It was like an oasis in a desert. The travellers walked fast to reach there.

On reaching the tree, the travellers heaved a sigh of relief. They dropped their luggage on the ground

and lay down under the shady tree.

The pleasant breeze of the neem tree refreshed the travellers. They then began feeling hungry.

One of the travellers looked up towards the tree and said, "This neem tree is really useless. It bears only small bitter fruits which can not be eaten."

The other man replied, "You are absolutely right. I'm unable to understand why people plant such useless trees. It's just a wastage of space."

The tree, which was listening to the travellers' conversation, thought with a tinge of sorrow, "These people are enjoying my shade, but are at the same time calling me useless. They are really ungrateful!"

We should be grateful to those who give us even something small.

The Mice and the Elephants

Once upon a time, a deadly epidemic broke out in a distant village. The people of the village deserted it and went away to live in another place. Few mice made this village their home. Soon the deserted village became the fort of the mice.

Near the village, there was a big forest. In the forest there lived a big group of elephants. Once there was an acute scarcity of water in the forest. The elephants who needed a lot of water to drink and bathe, found it extremely difficult to survive.

One day, one of the elephants informed their leader that there was a big lake near a village. This village was the same village where the mice were living.

The leader immediately instructed his followers to proceed towards the lake. All the elephants rushed enthusiastically and crossed the village running. While

running, they unknowingly trampled hundreds of mice under their feet. After drinking water, they returned through the same way. And again, a big number of mice were killed.

The worried and grieved mice ran to their king and pleaded with him to save them.

The mouse king along with some other mice went to the leader of the elephants and apprised him with their misery. The leader of the elephant said, "O dear friends! I did not know that by passing through your

village we were causing such a grave harm to you. I promise to you that now onwards we will change our way to reach the lake."

The mouse king thanked the elephants and came back to his place.

Shortly after this incidence, once the elephants were passing through the jungle along with their leader. The leader and a few other elephants fell prey to the

poachers' trap. They tried and tried but could not come out of the trap. Suddenly the troubled leader remembered the mice, who were living in the nearby village.

The leader sent one of his fellow elephants to inform the mice about the mishap. The messenger elephant ran as fast as he could and reached the village. There he gave his leader's message to the king of the mice.

The mice were very grateful to the mighty elephants for their kind gesture. In no time, hundreds of mice rushed to the rescue of their mighty friends.

After reaching there, the mice nibbled the ropes tied on the elephants' feet. The elephants were freed before the poachers could arrive. The mighty elephants thanked their small friends for their help, and remain friends forever.

> **No one is too small to help another at the hour of need.**

The Greedy Jackal

Once a hungry jackal was wandering in search of food. Suddenly he noticed a boar who was being chased by a hunter. The hunter targeted the boar and shot the arrow. The arrow hit the boar in his stomach. The wounded boar cried in pain and counter attacked the hunter with his tusk. The hunter was not prepared for this sudden attack and fell down. The angry boar forcefully hit the hunter with his sharp tusk and wounded him too.

The hunter and the boar were lying wounded near each other. The jackal saw both the hunter and the boar dying and became very happy.

He thought, "These two dead bodies will provide me enough food for many days". Suddenly he noticed the leather string of the bow lying beside the hunter.

After seeing so much of food, the jackal became greedy. He thought, "If I pass today's day by eating this string, I can save the food for one more day".

So he went near the bow and started chewing the string. The bow, which was under extreme tension, sprang back and hit the jackal severely. The jackal died immediately.

Greed often ends in misfortune.

The Two Goats

In a mountainous region, a river flowed between two lush green hills. A narrow bridge connected the two hills.

One day, two goats came on the bridge from opposite sides at the same time to cross the river. They encountered each other in the middle of the bridge. The bridge was so narrow that at a time only one goat could pass from there.

Both the goats wanted to cross the river first. But very soon they realized that it was not possible.

And if they fought over it, both of them would fall into the swirling river water.

So one of the two goats sat on the bridge and allowed the other goat to cross the bridge over his body. Afterwards, the goat who sat down also got up and crossed the bridge safely.

Confrontation should be avoided in larger interest.

The Cows and the Tiger

In a deep forest, there lived four cow friends. They always lived together. Wherever they went, they all went in a group. In spite of living amidst the wild animals, no one could ever dare to harm them due to their unity.

A tiger was aspiring to feast upon these cows for quite sometime. But whenever he tried, he was driven away by all the four by their joint efforts.

One day, the cows had a big quarrel. That day, each one went alone in a different direction to graze. The tiger got the right opportunity. He attacked the cows one by one and ate them up.

United we stand, divided we fall.

The Strange Reward

There was a noble king who loved and cared for his subjects. The king was a great patron of the artists. Artists from far off places came to see the king. But the chief of the guards, posted at the gate of the court was involved in corrupt practices. The dishonest chief did not allow the visitors to enter the court without taking a bribe.

One day, a folk singer came to meet the king. When he tried to enter through the palace gate, the guard stopped him and asked for the bribe. The folk singer did not like it. He did not even have any money to pay. He said, "Sir! I am a poor old man. At present,

I don't have any money. However, I'm confident that the king will surely reward me after hearing my song. I promise you that I'll hand over half of the reward to you." The chief of the guard agreed.

The man went in the king's court and sang a beautiful melodious song there. The king liked the song very much. He offered the man to ask for the reward he wanted.

The singer replied, "Your Majesty! If you are happy, then ask your servant to give one hundred lashes on my bare back as my reward."

His strange request surprised everyone. However, as the singer himself had asked for it, the king called

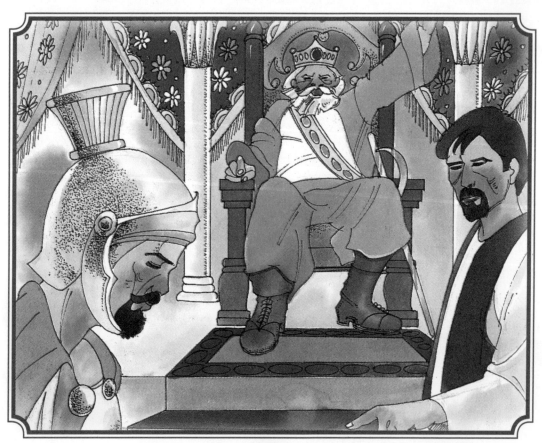

his servant with the whip and ordered him to give one hundred lashes on his back.

When the servant came with the whip and was about to start, the singer stopped him, "Wait! I have promised my partner to give equal share of my reward. I would like to give him his share first." The singer turned towards the king and urged him to call the chief of the guards. He then told him the whole episode related to the demand of bribe.

The king was enraged to hear this. He immediately summoned the dishonest chief of the guards. When he appeared in the court, the king asked his servant to give fifty lashes on his back. The dishonest chief was sent to the jail then.

The king happily gave the singer rich rewards and thanked him to bring a corrupt practitioner to his notice.

A wise man is not easily fooled.

The Mouse and the Bull

Once in a summer afternoon a mouse came out of his hole and saw a bull fast asleep under a tree. The loud snoring of the bull evoked the curiosity of the mouse.

He came close to the bull and saw the large nostrils. The inquisitive mouse entered into it and bit inside just for fun.

The bull awoke and bellowed in pain. The frightened mouse ran from there. The angry bull chased him with all his might. The mouse ran fast and managed to get into a hole of a nearby wall.

However, the raged bull was not ready to give up. He angrily bellowed, "You little silly creature, I'll teach you a lesson for daring to trouble a mighty bull."

The mouse said, "O mighty bull, I didn't want to trouble you. I bit you just for fun."

But the bull was intent on punishing the tiny mouse. He angrily dashed his head against the wall. The wall was strong. The bull dashed the wall many times but it did not give way. Observing his anger and desperation the mouse mocked, "You foolish mighty thing! Why are you breaking your head just for a trivial matter? It's not always necessary that you strong, big fellows would get everything you wish."

The bull did not like it. However he realized the truth in the words of the mouse. So he walked away quietly from there.

Might may not be always right.

Jungles without Animals

There was a king. He was very much fond of hunting. However, the king's hobby of hunting was causing a great loss to the jungles of the kingdom. The forests were getting bereft of animals.

The king's wise prime minister was sad and disappointed over the development. He was in search of the right opportunity to make the king concerned about it.

One day, the king went for hunting with his cavalcade. The prime minister who was also there, pretended as if he understood the birds' languages.

On the way, a group of parrots was twittering aloud. The king asked his prime minister, "Can you

tell me what they are talking about?"

The prime minister said, "Your Majesty! This group of parrots comprises both bride and groom sides and they are discussing about the marriage formalities.

The groom's father wants five jungles, which are totally bereft of birds and animals, as dowry. While the bride's father is happily assuring him that he will be giving not only five but ten empty jungles as dowry."

The king asked curiously, "Then what is the groom's father saying?"

The prime minister replied, "Your Majesty! Groom's father wants to know how he can get ten barren forests in a short span of time, as presently there are not so many empty jungles."

The prime minister continued further, "The bride's father is assuring the groom's father that as the king of this kingdom has great charm for hunting, very soon there will not be any difficulty in getting ten empty jungles. His hobby of hunting will soon empty a few more forests, as empty them without any animals and birds."

The minister cleverly conveyed the message to the king. The king realized the magnitude of loss being caused to the jungles due to his hobby. He immediately put a check on his hunting spree.

Protect animals to protect your world.

The Smell and the Sound

After finishing his day's work, a poor building labour was on his way back home. While passing through the market he came across the aroma of the delicious sweets. The smell was coming from the nearby sweetmeat shop.

Since the smell was mouth watering, the poor man stopped by the shop. He wanted to buy the sweets. However, it was not affordable for him. After waiting for a while, the man turned to go. Just then, a sudden stern voice stopped him, "Wait! Before you go, make the payment." It was the shopkeeper.

The poor man was astonished to hear this. He asked, "Payment! What kind of payment?" "Payment for the sweetmeat," said the shopkeeper. "But when did I eat your sweetmeat?" asked the man.

"You did not eat the sweetmeat. But, you did enjoy the pleasant smell of the sweets for quite a long time," said the cunning shopkeeper, "Smelling is as good as eating. So you must pay for it."

The poor man was upset to hear this. At some distance, a wise man was standing. He overheard their conversation. The wise man called the poor man and whispered something in his ears.

The poor man's eyes twinkled. He went into the shop. There he jingled the coins in his pocket for some time. The shopkeeper's eyes shone to hear the jingle of the coins. He said, "Hurry up, pay the money fast".

The poor man replied, "I've already paid the

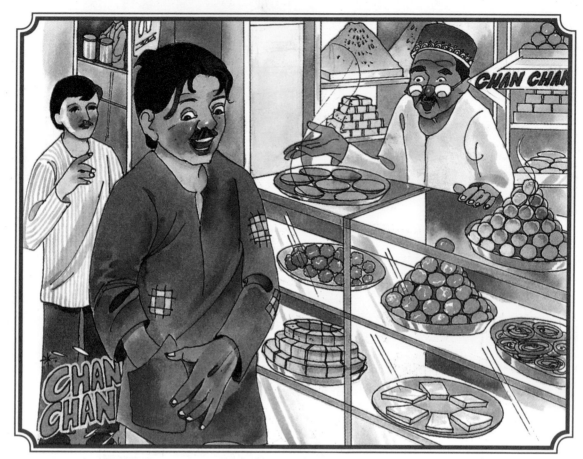

money. Didn't you get that?"

The shopkeeper shouted angrily, "When did you pay the money?"

"Just now! Didn't you hear the jingle of the coins? If smelling is as good as eating, then hearing the jingle sound of the coins is as good as receiving the money," replied the man.

The poor man smiled proudly and went away from there.

Tit for tat.

The Two Parrots

One-day a hunter caught two chicks from a parrot's nest. He put both the chicks in a cage. After a few days, one of the chicks slipped out of the opened cage door and flew away. The other chick remained with the hunter. The first chick flew to a sage's hut and took shelter there.

The hunter had friendship with many notorious criminals and robbers. They would often visit his house and hatch the plans of robbery. The parrot had been seeing those notorious visitors everyday and learning their language.

One day, a king came to the forest for hunting. While chasing a deer, he came close to the hunter's hut. The parrot cried out sharply, "A visitor is coming! Be ready to rob him!" Scared with these remarks, the

king pulled the rein and rode away swiftly. The parrot's call chased him from behind, "Kill him! Kill him! He is running away."

After trotting some distance, the king came across yet another hut. Outside the hut, there was a parrot sitting. The parrot spoke in a sweet voice, "Welcome, O honourable guest! Please come inside and sit comfortably." The king was amazed to see such a

well-mannered parrot.

That very moment, a sage came out of the hut and welcomed the king. It was the hut of a sage. The parrot again said, "Please drink cold water and have some fruits".

Then the king could not remain quiet. He asked the sage, "O learned man! I met a similar looking parrot in the hut of a hunter. The parrot was rude. He was speaking in foul and threatening language. Here, I am seeing this parrot who speaks nicely and is very well behaved. Why is this difference?"

The sage smiled, "It's because of the company in which the birds are living. Here, this parrot listens to the nice and gentle words. So, he is learning the same. Perhaps the other parrot is in the contact of wrong people and thus learning their language."

Always live in a good company as it has a great impact on our personality and behaviour

Then the king could not remain quiet. He asked the sage, "O learned man! I met a similar looking parrot in the hut of a hunter. The parrot was rude. He was speaking in foul and threatening language. Here, I am seeing this parrot who speaks nicely and is very well behaved. Why is this difference?"

The sage smiled, "It's because of the company in which the birds are living. Here, this parrot listens to the nice and gentle words. So, he is learning the same. Perhaps the other parrot is in the contact of wrong people and thus learning their language."

> **Always live in a good company as it has a great impact on our personality and behaviour.**

Once a wolf picked up a lamb from a sheep herd and ran away to a safe place. He offloaded the lamb from his shoulders and was about to kill him. Just then the lamb said, "I know that in the next few moments, I'll be killed. Would you please fulfil my last wish before eating me?"

The wolf stopped and asked, "What is your last wish?"

The lamb replied, "I am told that you are a wonderful flute player. I am very much fond of the sweet music of the flute. I would like to die after hearing this melodious music."

The wolf believed him and began playing his flute.

After playing for sometime when the wolf stopped, the lamb grinned and said, "Marvelous! Never before, I have heard such a beautiful piece of music. I'm very much sure that no one else can play the flute like you. Please play it once more."

The words of praise made the wolf extremely happy. He picked up the flute and played it once again, quite enthusiastically. This time the sound was louder than before.

The sound of the flute reached the shepherd and his dogs. They immediately rushed to the place. The dogs chased and caught the wolf.

The lamb swiftly escaped from there and reached his herd safely.

Never lose your cool in adversity.

Choosing the Next Ruler

There was a king. The king had two sons and a daughter. The elder son loved to enjoy his life leisurely. Most of the time, he was busy in horse racing. The second son liked hunting and spent a good amount of time in the forest, chasing the animals.

The king was getting old. So he wanted to decide about his successor. One day, he called his wise minister to discuss about the successor for his throne.

When the minister came, the king asked, "Tell me whom should I make my successor? The elder or the younger son?"

The minister thought for a while and then replied, "I beg your pardon Your Majesty! None of your sons

have the ability to become an able king. A king should be concerned about the problems and the needs of his subjects. Unfortunately, both the princes have no time to look after the subjects of your kingdom. Your Majesty, according to me, the princess best suits this post. She spends her time with the people of your kingdom and is concerned about their problems. She really works hard for their welfare. People like their princess very much. According to me, the throne should go to a person like her, who is sensitive about the people's cause."

The minister's words appealed to the king. He decided to go against the custom of making a son the successor and happily chose his able daughter as the future queen of his kingdom.

A good ruler should be concerned about his people.

In a village, there lived four childhood friends. Three of them were learned and had acquired knowledge from Varanasi, the centre place of knowledge. The fourth friend was not a learned person, but he had good common sense.

One day, the three learned friends decided to go to an opportune place where they could get a chance to grow and utilize their knowledge. Since the fourth friend was their childhood friend, they also took him with them.

On the way to their destination, they had to pass through a forest. When they were in the forest, they

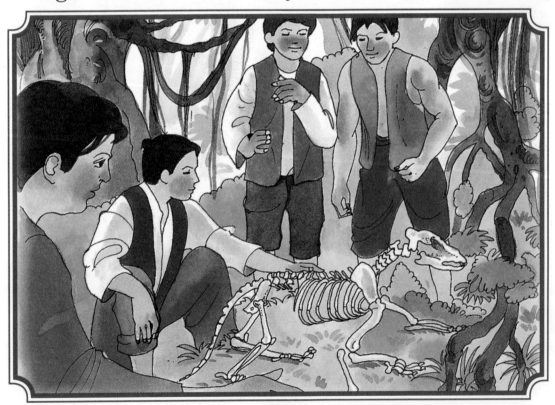

came across the bones of a dead animal, which was lying on the ground. The friends stopped there. One of them said, "We are going to the city to prove our knowledge. Here we have a chance to practice our knowledge. Let's bring the animal back to its life."

Everyone agreed. They all collected the bones and assembled them at one place.

The first friend said, "With the help of my knowledge, I can reconstruct the skeleton of the animal." He then used his knowledge, chanted some mantra and a big skeleton of an animal was in front of them.

The second friend said, "I know how to add flesh and skin to this skeleton." The second friend used his

knowledge and chanted some mantra. The skeleton got the flesh and skin and a dead lion was lying in front of them.

Eager to prove his knowledge, the third friend said, "I can bring this dead lion to life with the help of my knowledge."

The fourth friend, who remained silent spectator till then, screamed promptly, "No-No! Don't do that. This is a lion. If he comes alive, he'll certainly kill all of us."

The other three friends mocked at him and said, "It'll be better if you keep yourself aside from our knowledgeable discussions."

The fourth friend said, "Alright! Do whatever you want to do. But let me first climb up on this tall tree, before you prove your knowledge any further." The fourth friend climbed up swiftly on the tree. The third learned friend chanted some mantra and brought the lion back to the life. The lion rose up, roared loudly, and pounced upon them. After eating all three of them, the lion went away in the deep forest.

All the knowledge is useless if it is not used with proper common sense.

The Four Fools

There was a king. The king often behaved in a whimsical manner. One day in such a mood swing, he ordered his minister, "I want to see four fools. Each should excel in foolishness."

"As you wish Your Majesty!" replied the minister and went away in search of such fools. He walked on the roads of the city in search of the fools.

While roaming, the minister noticed a man who was walking hurriedly with a box of sweets in his hand. To see him in such a great hurry, the minister could

not resist himself from asking the reason for the same.

The man unwillingly answered, "See, I'm in great hurry. My estranged wife, who married some other man, has given birth to a child. On this happy occasion, I'm going to distribute sweets." After saying this, the man again started walking.

Hearing this, the minister said to himself, "I found at least one fool". He asked the man to come along with him. The man was not at all ready to comply, as he did not want to be late in celebrating the occasion. However, as it was a royal order, he had no choice but to accompany the minister.

On their way, when both of them were coming

back, the minister eyed upon a conspicuous sight. A man was riding on a horse's back carrying a stack of hay on his own head. The minister enquired, "Why are you carrying the stack on your head, instead of placing it on the horse's back?"

The man on the horse said, "Sir, this horse is like my family member. He is already burdened with my weight. How can I make him carry the additional load of the stack on his back? To relieve him from this extra burden, I'm carrying the load on my own head."

Hearing this, the minister directed the man to accompany him. Then all the three went to the king's court. The minister introduced both the fools with their

acts of foolishness to the king. The king enjoyed it. He then asked, "Where are the other two fools?"

"The other two fools are present here Your Majesty!" said the minister.

"Where are they?" asked the king quite surprised.

"Your Majesty! The third fool is I who wasted the time and energy in such a futile exercise," said the minister.

"And where is the fourth fool?" asked the king who was quite apprehensive by then.

"I beg your pardon, Your Majesty! The fourth and the biggest fool is yourself Your Majesty, who put me on such a worthless assignment?" quipped the minister.

To indulge in a futile work is an act of foolishness.

The Peacock and the Crane

A peacock was extremely proud of his looks. He would admire his own beauty in front of other birds. He would boastfully say, "Look at me! How beautiful are my feathers and tail. I'm the most beautiful bird in this world."

The proud peacock would dance merrily spreading his long colourful feathers.

One day, he went near the forest lake. There he met a crane. Seeing the crane, the peacock mocked at him, "What colourless feathers you have! You look so ordinary!"

The crane replied humbly, "Of course your feathers are colourful, bright and beautiful. But with your feathers, you cannot fly high up. However my colorless, plain feathers have the strength to carry me up in the high sky."

Worthless beauty is not appreciable.

The Friends and the bear

Mangal and Chandu were two good friends. They used to spend a good amount of time together. One day, they were passing through a forest near their village. Suddenly they saw a bear coming towards them.

Mangal knew climbing. So he hurriedly climbed up a tall tree to his safety. Chandu did not know how to climb a tree. However, Mangal did not bother about his friend Chandu.

Chandu stood there helplessly for few moments. Suddenly an idea flashed in his mind. He had heard

that the wild animals did not touch a dead body. So Chandu applied his wisdom and lay down on the ground as a dead person.

Soon the bear reached there. He sniffed Chandu's face and thought him dead. The bear did not touch Chandu and went on his way.

After sometime, Mangal climbed down from the tree and asked Chandu, "What did the bear say in your ears, when you were lying?"

Chandu replied bitterly, "He told me to keep away from selfish friends like you".

Keep away from opportunists.

The Boy and the Wolf

There was a shepherd boy. Everyday he would go up the hill to graze the sheep herd. One day, just to have fun he shouted, "Wolf! Help! Wolf! Help!"

Down the hill, the farmers were working in their field. They heard his cry for help and at once rushed to the boy. But there was no wolf.

The boy giggled to see the anxious farmers. The boy's mischief annoyed the farmers. They warned him against playing such trick.

After a few days, the boy again played the same mischief. The farmers once again ran to his help. But they did not find any wolf there and returned angrily.

Next day, a wolf indeed approached there. The boy climbed up the tree for his safety and shouted for help to save his sheep from the wolf.

But no one came there as the farmers thought that the silly boy was again playing the same trick. The wolf killed many sheep and the boy watched it helplessly.

> **Keep away from lying. Once known as a liar, you will never be taken seriously.**

The Ugly Tree

In a forest, there was a crooked tree amidst the tall and straight trees. The crooked tree often sighed for his ugly look. He enviously looked at the other tall and slender trees and felt sad for his unpleasant look.

One day a woodcutter came to the forest to cut the wood. The woodcutter cut down few long straight trees. Then he came across the twisted tree. The

woodcutter looked at the crooked branches and said, "This tree is of no use! It's better not to cut this."

The woodcutter went ahead sparing the crooked tree. The tree thanked his crookedness. Never again did he sigh about his ugliness in the future.

Everything has its own advantage and disadvantage Accept it happily.

The Number of Crows

Birbal was the star courtier in the court of Akbar. Akbar was also very fond of Birbal for his super intelligence and wit. The other courtiers were always jealous of Birbal. One day, a group of

courtiers decided to let Birbal down in front of Akbar.

When everyone, including Birbal was sitting in the court, the senior most courtier appealed to the king, "Your Majesty! You always praise Birbal for his cleverness. If he is so intelligent, then he must tell the court how many crows are present in our kingdom."

Emperor Akbar smiled and looked towards Birbal. Birbal replied instantaneously, "There are nine thousand nine hundred ninety five crows in our kingdom".

Everyone in the court was astonished to hear his prompt reply.

"Are you sure? If this number doesn't match with the actual number of crows present in the city, then?" asked the Emperor.

Birbal replied coolly, "Your Majesty! My counting is appropriate. If at any time the number of crows is found less, then it will indicate that few of the crows are out of the city to visit their friends and relatives."

Birbal further said, "And if the number of crows is more than what I have counted, then it will reflect that a few crows from other places have come to visit our city."

"In any case, my counting is absolutely right," Birbal said firmly.

The envious courtiers were startled to hear this. There was no way out to defy his claim. They were at their wit's end and looked foolishly towards each other.

However, the Emperor laughed aloud to hear his clever reply.

> A tricky question has a tricky answer.

The Two Mice

A country mouse and a town mouse were good friends. One day, the country mouse invited the town mouse at his place. The town mouse accepted his invitation and came to stay with him for few a days.

The country mouse was happy to see his friend and welcomed him warmly. He served different crops of the farm and a variety of fruits. They enjoyed the food peacefully in the field.

However, after staying there for a few days, the town mouse said, "What a plain and simple life you are leading here! The food you eat here is tasteless and life is charmless. Come to my town and see the

wonderful life I'm leading there." So the country mouse decided to accompany his friend to the town.

The town mouse lived in the kitchen of a big house. The town mouse welcomed his friend with many delicious items like cake, biscuits and bread. The food appeared tasty. Both the friends sat to eat. As soon as then began eating, they heard the footsteps of the lady of the house.

Both of them swiftly ran to their hideouts. After sometime when the lady went out of the kitchen, they returned and sat to eat again. Hardly had they enjoyed the tasty cake, they heard the footsteps of another resident of the house.

The two friends again ran to their hole. The country mouse was quite irritated by this continuous threat. He said to the town mouse, "You enjoy your cakes and biscuits. I don't want to lead a life, which

is not peaceful. Your life is pathetic. I'm going back from here."

And the country mouse returned to his village.

All the material riches can not provide happiness in life.

The Warrior and the Horse

During a battle, a warrior fought bravely and caused great damage to the enemy side. His loyal horse helped him a lot. Whenever he was cordoned off by the enemies, it was his loyal horse, who protected the warrior and took him out safely with his swiftness and great speed.

When the battle ended, the warrior got medals and rewards for his bravery. People praised him for his

bravery and he was famed as the hero. The warrior was happy and proud. He was very well aware of the great contributions of his horse in his success and fame. So, the warrior loved his pet and took good care of him.

After sometime the neighbouring kingdoms made peace. During peace, the soldiers were no more required. So, the warrior returned to his farm and started working there. The warrior used his horse to help him in farming.

Slowly and slowly, the soldier forgot the contributions of his horse in his fame and success. He started treating him like any other ordinary cattle. The warrior even stopped giving him good food.

The whole day's hard work without any good food, transformed the strong and agile horse into a weak and inefficient animal. He was no more strong and zealous.

One day, the warrior got a message from the king that war had again started and he was required there. He then remembered his loyal horse, as he needed him in the battleground.

But, the horse had become weak and slow. He was no more useful for him. The warrior remorsed for not taking proper care of him.

"Once this horse saved my life and made me a war hero. But I forgot his contributions. Today, I remembered him because I need his help. I'm selfish and ungrateful," the warrior repented. He sat down holding his head in his hands.

Don't ignore the contributions of others, else you will lose it for future.

The Wolf and the Three Sheep

Surly, Burly and Curly were three sheep brothers. They all lived in a beautiful straw house.

One day, there came a wicked wolf to live close to their place. The sheep brothers were frightened to see him. The brothers knew that the wolf could attack on them at any time.

Surly the eldest one said, "We must prepare ourselves against the danger. Our beautiful house is flimsy and it can not protect us from the wolf."

Burly and Curly agreed with him. They all went to the market to bring the material to build a solid strong house, where they could live safely.

Soon they built a strong stone house with their joint efforts.

The wolf was in search of an opportunity to kill the sheep for long. One day, he went to the house of the three brothers. The wolf knocked at the door. The brothers were careful and did not open the door. The angry wolf dashed his head on the door to break into the house. But the wolf himself was hurt in turn.

The frustrated and angry wolf climbed on the roof of the house and tried to enter through the chimney.

The sheep brothers were far too smart for the wolf. They had guessed that the wolf could enter from the chimney. So they prepared a fire in the fireplace below the chimney. Curly asked his brother Burly to provide few more logs in the fireplace.

As soon as the wolf entered through the chimney, he slid into the burning fireplace. The wolf was engulfed in the flames and died at once.

A careful planning can even restrict a strong enemy.

The Cat and the Fox

Once a cat and a fox were sitting leisurely and were chatting about the threat of the hounds.

"The hounds are horrifying. I just don't like them," said the fox.

"Yes, you are right! I too don't like this scary creature," agreed the cat.

"The hounds are agile and fast runners. But I'm sure that they shall not be able to catch me. I've learnt a number of tricks to protect myself from the hounds," said the fox.

"What are these tricks?" asked the cat.

"There are many!" replied the fox quite boastfully. "I can run through the prickly plants to save myself. I can swiftly hide amidst the bushes and can even hide in burrows. There are many more such tricks," said the fox with a swollen pride.

"I know only one good trick to save myself from the hounds," said the cat.

"Only one trick! How sad of you! However, what's it?" asked the fox in quite a consoling tone.

"I can climb up a tree to get away from them and I'm going to perform it now," said the cat, "Look behind, the hounds are approaching".

The cat swiftly climbed up a nearby tree to her safety.

The fox too ran and applied his tricks one after another to save himself from the chasing hounds. But none of his tricks could work. Ultimately the hounds caught him and killed him.

Sitting safely on the branches of the tree, the cat whispered, "My only trick is indeed worthwhile compared to the many tricks of the poor fox!"

It's always advisable to accomplish oneself in a chosen domain than casually involving in many.

The Crows and the Pigeon

A farmer was troubled by the menace of a flock of crows. Everyday the big flock of crows would arrive in his cornfield and would destroy the crop.

One day, upset with the heavy loss, the farmer threw a net in his cornfield. As usual, the crows came to eat the grains and were caught in the net.

The happy farmer lifted the net from his field. The farmer was rejoiced to see the trouble makers in his trap. The crows were desperately trying to come out of the net. The farmer screamed happily, "At last, you fell in my trap. Soon you will meet your end."

Suddenly, he eyed a pigeon. He was very much surprised to see a pigeon in the crows' flock. The farmer asked, "What are you doing with these evil crows?"

The pigeon requested the farmer, "Please leave me! I did not come to steal your grains. I had just accompanied them."

The farmer replied, "That may be true. Now that you are found in this evil gang, you too will not be spared."

The farmer called his hounds. They came running and killed all the birds including the poor pigeon.

> **One is known by the company he keeps.**
> **Be careful in choosing it.**

The Foolish Bodygaurd

Once upon a time, there was a king. The king had a pet monkey. The monkey was very loyal to the king. So, he appointed the monkey as his personal bodyguard.

The wise courtiers suggested to the king, not to entrust such a big responsibility on a mere monkey since he could not be as wise and sensible as a human being. However, the king did not pay any heed to their wise suggestions. The monkey was appointed as the king's personal bodyguard.

One day the king was tired. So he instructed his bodyguard, "I am going to sleep. Ensure that no one

disturbs me in between." The king went to sleep and the monkey began guarding carefully.

Suddenly, he saw a fly entering the bedroom through the window. He tried to drive it out, but he did not succeed. The fly sat on the king's bed. The monkey drove the fly from there. The fly then sat on the king's hand. It was again driven by the monkey. But this time, the fly landed on the king's neck.

The monkey was tired and frustrated. He could not tolerate it anymore. He instantly picked up the king's sword, kept beside the bed and tried to hit the fly. The tiny fly swiftly flew away from the king's neck and the loyal foolish monkey ended up his loyalty by cutting his master's neck.

A clever enemy is better than a foolish friend.

The Cost of Happiness

There was a cobbler. He was a poor, but happy man. He worked hard the whole day . However, he was never seen anxious. He had a habit of singing, when he was totally engrossed in his work.

A rich man lived near the hut of the cobbler. He was jealous to see the poor cobbler leading a peaceful and happy life.

One day, the rich man went to the cobbler. He gave him a bag of money and said, "I've enough money. So I've decided to give a part of my wealth to the poor and needy."

The cobbler accepted the money happily. But then on, he was always anxious about the safety of his wealth. The cobbler forgot to sing happily.

The envious rich man laughed in his heart at the success of his plan. He was happy to snatch away the cobbler's peace of mind.

Everything has its cost.

The Boy and the Vendor

There was a clever vendor. He sold roasted groundnuts. Children were very fond of the nuts and they would usually come to buy roasted nuts from him. Quite often the clever vendor would give less amount of nuts and fooled the children with his glib talk.

One day, a boy came to buy nuts. As usual the vendor gave the child less groundnuts.

The boy asked the vendor, "You have given me less nuts sir!"

The sly vendor replied, "Lesser nuts will be easier to carry my dear!"

The boy didn't say anything. He took out a few coins from his pocket and placed them on the vendor's palm.

The vendor counted the money and found it less.

The vendor said, "You have given me less money my dear!"

The boy replied, "Yes I know sir! Less money will be easier for you to count."

Over smart people are likely to be outsmarted.

Lazy Servents

An old woman had the habit of waking up before sunrise. Early in the morning when the cock crowed, she would rise up from the bed.

The woman had two servants. Both were lazy. They did not like to wake up early in the morning. But the lady was very strict. As soon as the cock started crowing, she would wake them up. She hurried them to start their work.

The servants were quite fed up with their mistress's early morning call. One day one of them said to the other, "We must kill the cock to get a longer and undisturbed sleep. Our mistress wakes up on hearing the crowing cock. When the cock is not there, she won't be able to wake up so early. And if she herself does not wake up early, then no one will disturb our sleep."

The other servant also liked the idea. They killed the cock on the next day. Now that the cock was not there, the old lady did not have the way to know the appropriate time to wake up. The lady was now more attentive. She started waking up earlier than before. Once she got up from her bed, she would immediately call her servants to wake up.

The servants' idea backfired on them and they faced tougher time ahead.

> **Wrong means can't yield a right result.**

Chintu and Cashew Nuts

A boy named Chintu liked cashew nuts very much. His mother knew this very well. So she everyday gave him a few cashew nuts to eat. But Chintu always wanted to eat more.

Whenever his mother placed few cashew nuts on his palm, Chintu would insist, "Mom, give me more!"

However every time his mother said, "My dear,

too many cashew nuts at a time will cause pain in your stomach. Cashew nuts are good when they are eaten in small quantity."

Though Chintu would not say anything, he was not at all convinced with his mother. He always believed that his mother did not want to give him more cashew nuts and therefore she made an excuse.

One day, Chintu's mother had gone to the market and Chintu was all alone in the house. He somehow managed to reach the jar, placed in the kitchen. That day, he ate as many cashew nuts as he could. There was no one to prevent him.

However, just after few hours of eating the cashew nuts, Chintu had a severe stomachache. While crying in pain, he repented not heeding his mother's advice.

Always obey your elders.

Dangerous Curiosity

Once a snake charmer caught a snake and kept it in a bamboo basket. The snake tried hard to come out of it, but he could not.

In the snake charmer's house, there lived a young rat. The rat was very naughty and mischievous. He was always curious about the things lying around him. However, mother rat always cautioned her young son not to touch any unfamiliar objects.

One day, the young rat came out of his hole and saw a bamboo basket lying in the corner. The basket appeared very attractive to him. So, the curious rat went closer and climbed over it. He tried to peep inside to get a clue about the contents of the basket. However the dense weaving of the box prevented him from peeping inside.

Now the restless rat was even more curious. He guessed, "It seems that sweets are kept inside. If somehow I open the basket, I can enjoy the sweets."

The rat tried and tried, but did not succeed in opening it. Tired of his efforts to open the basket, the curious rat started cutting the bamboo basket with his sharp teeth. Finally he succeeded in making a small hole.

The snake was sitting inside the basket waiting for the right opportunity to come out.

Finally, the young curious fellow entered into the box through the hole and was immediately gobbled up by the snake sitting inside. The snake came out of the basket and glided back to the forest.

Don't be over enthusiastic about any unknown object.

The Frogs and the Bull

It was the rainy season. The village pond was overflowing with water. The tiny frogs were hopping and playing there merrily.

A bull walked to the pond to quench his thirst. After drinking water, the bull bellowed with satisfaction. His loud bellow frightened the tiny frogs. Never before they had seen a bull.

The scared tiny ones hurried to their grandfather. The gasping little frogs said, "Grandpa, today we saw a huge animal at the pond!"

Grandpa was the eldest of all the frogs. His pride

was hurt to hear this. He at once dilated his chest, stretched his legs, puffed his cheeks and asked, "Was the animal at the pond bigger than this?"

The grandchildren said in chorus, "Much bigger, Grandpa!"

The grandfather dilated his chest further and with this increased size, he again asked the same question. But the children repeated their answer.

The proud grandfather dilated his chest more and more. But the children gave the same answer. Finally unable to expand any more, the grandfather's lungs burst and he died.

Impractical pride is foolishness.

The Clever Crow

Once a crow found a big piece of cheese. The crow comforted herself on a branch of a big tree before eating it. That very moment a hungry fox passed by the tree.

When the fox saw the piece of cheese, his mouth watered. He wondered, "Somehow I should get this piece of cheese!"

An idea flashed in his mind. The fox said in a very gentle voice, "Dear madam crow! I've heard that your voice is very sweet and melodious. Would you please oblige me with a song?"

But the crow was far smarter. She carefully placed the cheese under her foot and then asked, "Shall I sing now?"

The outwitted fox passed from there quietly.

Be careful of flattery.

The Partridge and the Ant

On the bank of a river, there was a tree. On one of its branches, there lived a partridge.

One day when the partridge was sitting on the tree, he saw an ant flowing in the river water. The ant was crying for help. The partridge took pity on the helpless ant. He plucked a leaf and placed it near the flowing ant.

The ant got support and climbed on the leaf. The partridge then picked up the leaf along with the ant and dropped it on the land.

The ant thanked the partridge for saving his life and went back in the groove of the tree where he stayed.

One day, the partridge was taking an afternoon nap while sitting on the tree. That very time, a hunter

came from somewhere and saw the partridge. The hunter stringed his bow to shoot an arrow at the partridge. The ant at once bit the hunter on his toe. The hunter cried in pain and lost the grip on the bow. Hearing the cry, the partridge woke up and flew away.

> **Good deed is always returned with good deed.**

The Foolish Monkeys

On a hill forest there lived a group of monkeys. The whole day they jumped from one tree to another under the sun. When the winter came and the snowfall started, the monkeys who lived on the trees, were unable to tolerate the cold nights.

The monkeys had some idea about the fire, but they did not know what exactly it was. So they mistook the red fruits of the jungle as the fire. They plucked the fruits and assembled them on the ground. Then they made a big heap of the dry leaves and twigs to burn with the help of the red fruits. Few of the monkeys even started blowing near the heap with bamboo pipes.

A small bird was sitting on the adjacent tree and was watching their efforts. The bird laughed and said, "O foolish monkeys! You are trying to create the fire without a spark. These red fruits can never give you fire."

The foolish monkeys did not listen to the wise words of the little bird. They rather became angry that the tiny bird pretended to be very smart.

Monkeys screamed, "Keep quiet! Who are you to speak in our matters? We do not want your suggestion."

The little bird was unable to digest the foolishness of those monkeys. Though the monkeys were not at all ready to listen to her, she kept on advising them.

At last, irritated by her continuous twittering, one of the monkeys caught hold of her and threw her down on the hard rock. The bird died immediately.

Unwanted suggestions never get honoured.

The Wise Cap Seller

There was once a cap seller, who moved from one village to other to sell his beautiful caps.

One day, while going to another village, he passed through a jungle. There were many monkeys in that jungle.

After walking for a long distance, the cap seller got tired. So he lay down under a shady tree. Soon he fell asleep.

When the cap seller woke up, he found his box of caps open and the caps missing. The poor cap seller was very upset. He was wondering where the caps could have gone in that lonely place.

Suddenly, a whooping sound coming from above attracted him. He looked up and was amazed to see the monkeys wearing his colourful caps.

The cap seller tried different ways to get back his caps, but nothing work out. Irritated by his failure, the cap seller picked up a stone and threw it towards the monkeys. At once monkeys picked fruits from the tree and threw them at the cap seller.

Suddenly a brilliant idea flashed through his mind.

Monkeys have the habit of imitating others. So the cap seller took off his cap and threw it on the ground.

The monkeys at once took off their own caps and threw them down as well.

The cap seller swiftly picked up all the caps and went away happily from there.

**Presence of mind finds
a way out of any adversity.**

The Fox and the Cock

One day, a fox was passing by a tree. He saw a cock sitting on a top branch of the tree. The fox's mouth watered. "What a fine lunch he could be!" thought the fox.

But the fox did not know how to climb the tree. So, he decided to befool the cock with his glib talk.

The fox looked up and said in a very gentle voice, "Hello friend! How are you? I have come here with a great news. Just now, I have heard about an order from heaven. God has commanded that all the birds and beasts will live happily without harming each other. Now onwards, foxes shall not eat any birds. Hence, there is no need to be afraid of each other. It's indeed a happy occasion. Come down, we'll celebrate it together."

The cock said, "It's really a wonderful news. It seems that this news has reached some other friends of us. Look behind! Hounds are coming to meet you."

The frightened fox was all set to run from there. The cock was amused to see this. He said, "Why are you scared of these hounds? We all are friends now! aren't we?"

The fox replied hurriedly, "Yes of course! But the hounds might not know this!" Saying thus the fox fled away as fast as he could.

Brainless Donkey

In a jungle, there lived a lion and his assistant jackal. The lion hunted the animals and the jackal helped the lion. After satisfying his own hunger, the lion used to give the residue of the prey to the jackal.

One day the lion broke his leg while fighting with a wild elephant. The lion could not hunt for many days.

Both the lion and the jackal were dying of hunger. So one day the lion advised jackal, "If you can manage to bring any animal here, then I will attack him and we both can satisfy our hunger".

The jackal went out in the search of an animal, whom he could fool to take near the lion. On the way he met a donkey. The jackal grinned and said, "O dear friend, I was in search of a suitable minister for the king lion and I think, you are just the right person for this post. Please come with me and grace the coveted post."

The donkey was after all a donkey. He could not see the plot behind jackal's statement and readily accompanied him. When they reached close to the lion, the lion pounced upon the donkey and killed him at once.

Both the lion and the jackal were happy on this success. When the lion was about to eat the donkey, he felt thirsty. He asked the jackal to guard the spoil and went to drink water from the nearby pond.

In the meanwhile, the hungry jackal who was unable to resist his hunger ate out the brain of the donkey.

When the lion returned and started eating the donkey, he found the brain missing. He asked angrily, "Where is the donkey's brain?"
The cunning jackal replied with folded hands, "Your majesty, the donkey does not have brain. If he had any, would he come here?"

A cunning person will always be cunning.

The Blue Fox

One day a fox could not get anything to eat in the jungle. He wandered in search of food. While wandering, the hungry fox crossed the jungle and entered in a village.

When he was roaming in the village, a group of dogs chased the stranger fox. The scared fox ran fast to save his life. On the way he fell down in a tub of blue colour dye.

After some time the fox came out of the tub cautiously and ran towards the jungle.

However, the fox did not notice that after jumping into the dye his body's colour had changed to blue.

When the fox was moving in the jungle, he met his fellow animals. He was utterly surprised to find that everybody was scared of him.

While passing by the jungle's pond, he saw his own image in the water and immediately understood the whole matter.

The hungry cunning fox thought of a brilliant plan. He climbed over a hill and started calling the animals of the jungle, "Dear friends! I have come from heaven. God has appointed me as your king. Now onwards, I'll take care of all your problems. Please do not be afraid."

Hearing his loud call, the animals assembled

there. The animals of the jungle, who had never seen such an animal, believed his words. They said, "Your majesty! Your wish is command for us. What can we do for you?"

The fox was happy that his plan had worked. The fox said, "You people should serve me well and take care of all my needs.

After that the life of the fox was completely changed. He did not have to bother about his food and other needs. Each and everything was made available at his doorsteps by the animals.

One day, a pack of foxes passed through his place. The foxes were howling loudly.

The blue fox, who had not howled since long, had a sudden strong urge for howling. He forgot everything and started howling aloud along with the other foxes.

Hearing his howl, the animals immediately recognized this self-declared heavenly creature. They all ran after the cunning fox and drove him out of the jungle.

Never try to hide your real identity to acquire a short time gain else you will have to pay heavily at the end.

The Loyal Servant

Once in a rich merchant's house, there worked a loyal servant. He was good hearted, sincere, and loved and respected his master dearly. There was just one problem with him. He often dozed off when he was supposed to be guarding his master's house in the afternoons.

One after noon he had a dream that a snake had slipped into his master's bedroom and had snuggled into his mattress.

The servant woke up with a jerk, ran to his master's bedroom, pushed his master from the bed and pulled out the mattress. When he did so, a sleeping snake fell off the mattress. The master and the servant picked up a stick and drove the snake away into the forest before it could harm anybody.

The master was shaken after the incident. He asked his servant, "How did you know there was a snake lying there?" The loyal servant's chest puffed up with pride. "Oh master!" he gloated, "When I was sitting outside the house, I dozed off and I had a dream. In the dream I saw the snake. I rushed in to save you as soon as I woke up."

The kind master simply smiled. "I must reward you for your goodness," he said. "Here, take this bag of coins." The servant was very pleased. "Thank-you master," he said.

"But," the master said, "There's no need for you

to come to work from tomorrow onwards. The servant was surprised. "But why master?" he asked surprised, "Did I not just save your life?"

"Yes you did," replied the master, "But if you had done your job well, the snake would never have entered the house in the first place, and you would never have had to save my life the way you did. You were supposed to guard the house. Instead you were sleeping and having dreams. I am grateful, but I don't think you are dutiful and I cannot risk it further, to have you employed here."

The loyal servant became sad. But he has learnt his lesson, and knowing that his master was right, left his home quietly.

> **Work should be considered worship,**
> **and never abused.**

The Merchant and the Traveller

Once upon a time in a village, there lived a rich merchant. He enjoyed getting together with people, sharing jokes and spending his time in meaningless trivialities.

One day a traveller who was passing by the merchant's village saw a tidy crowd collected under the market side, banyan tree. He walked up to the place and asked someone, "What is happening here?" "Oh! There's a lying competition in progress," replied his companion. "The man who tells the biggest lie, will be awarded by the rich oil merchant of the village, who is seated there," he said pointing to the merchant.

The traveller could not believe the stupidity, but listened to what was being said.

One man stood up and said, "Every day when I go to sleep I visit heaven. I stay there all night and come back in the morning." The audiences clapped and the man sat down beaming, sure that he had won.

Just then another man stood up. "I never eat," he announced to the crowd. "I once swallowed an entire watermelon, and now the seeds sow themselves in my stomach and a new fruit grows every time I feel hungry."

The audiences clapped loudly, and the merchant nodded his head approvingly. The traveller could not

believe his ears. He exclaimed, "Whoever conducts a contest like this, is the biggest fool in the world." Suddenly there was silence all around. The merchant looked at the traveller angrily. The traveller realised that he had thought out aloud and then smiling sheepishly said, "But sir, I thought this was a lying contest. And I believe I have just uttered the biggest lie of all. So, don't I deserve the award?"

The only way the merchant could save his reputation was by giving the traveller the pre-announced award of a bag of gold coins.

The traveller left there as soon as possible a richer and happier man, leaving behind a wiser merchant in his wake.

A fool is his own biggest enemy. presence of mind is a great friend.

The Good Minister

One upon a time in a rich kingdom there lived a kind king. He had a very intelligent minister. The king never did anything without consulting his minister.

But there was one thing about the minister which angered the king. The minister had the habit of saying, 'Everything happens for the best,' in every situation. The king did not agree that was the case. But he did not argue too much with the minister.

One day, as the king and his minister were enjoying a meal together, the king cut his finger and he was bleeding profusely. As the doctors attended to the king, the minister said, "Everything happens for the best!"

On hearing this, the king lost his temper. In a fit of rage he said, "Throw him in the dungeon. I will hang this ingrate minister next week."

The minister went with the guards quietly, only

saying his favourite line once again, "Everything happens for the best."

A couple of days later, the king came to meet the minister in his prison cell. "I am here to release you," he said. "Oh Maharaj thank-you," exclaimed the minister. "But why did you decide to do so? You were so angry with me the other day."

The king then told the minister a story. "Yesterday I went hunting and got lost in a forest," he explained. "A cannibal tribe caught hold of me. They were about to sacrifice me when they saw that I did not have one finger. They decided that I was not fit for sacrifice. So they spared me and I am alive today."

"Oh Maharaj," exclaimed the delighted minister,

"That's wonderful. I am very happy that you are safe and alive. After all 'Everything happens for the best.'

The king was slightly confused. "Tell me," he demanded, "You said it was best that my finger was cut off. And it was. It saved me. But why did you say everything happens for the best, when I put you in prison?"

"Maharaj think about it," explained the witty minister. "Had I been with you yesterday, the tribals would have sacrificed me."

The king laughed at his minister's comment. He also awarded him handsomely for being faithful and loyal to him, and was never angry with him, ever again.

Sometimes everything does happen for the best.

The Thief Who Trapped Himself

Ramu was a simple boy who sold wadas for a living. One day, as he began collecting his things to head home after a good sale, he found that his money was missing. He was very upset as he knew his parents were waiting for the money to buy food items for the house.

His friend Shyam passed by, and Ramu told him what had happened. Shyam was a very smart boy. He announced aloud, "Attention all. If you go into this room you will see a great new trick. One amongst us has robbed my friend's money, and I shall expose the thief in front of the whole crowd."

Soon a large crowd collected around Shyam's tent. He told the people who assembled there, "You must give me a fifty paise coin and then I shall let you enter."

The crowd was curious to know how a little boy would nab a seasoned robber. So, many of them presented him with a coin and entered the small tent.

Finally a man walked up and after much thought told Shyam, "Here is my coin. I want to see your trick as well." Immediately Shyam said, "This is the thief catch him, catch him!"

Before he realised it, the crowd had caught the thief. On emptying his pockets, several coins that

naturally belonged to Ramu, were found.

The elders asked Shyam, "How did you know this man was the thief. He entered the tent, like any of us." "Oh but uncle," Shyam explained, "His coin was oily. Ramu sold wadas, and his money always got oily. I knew whoever took the money would be the only one to have an oily coin. And this man did."

Ramu thanked his friend and went home happily. Thus Shyam's smartness and the thief's own stupidity did him in.

> **Even the smartest criminals leave some clue that can lead a smart person to them.**

The Tricky Tiger

A tiger once lived in a jungle. He was ferocious and cunning. One day after he had killed his prey, he found a large treasure upon the person of his victim. This gave the cunning tiger an idea, whereby he would get food, and never have to hunt for it again.

The tiger found a suitable place near the mud path of the jungle that had a road leading from one village to another. He bent his head weakly and laid out the treasure before him. He waited for a while in this manner.

When he saw a man passing by, he called out. "Oh kind sire, I am dying and wish to do one good deed before I pass away. I found this treasure and

want to give it to a deserving man. Of all the people I have met today, you seem to be the most deserving. Why don't you come over and take the treasure?"

The man eyed the treasure greedily. He thought, "The tiger looks good-natured. Why not take the treasure and be on my way? My wife will be very happy." Without realising the extent of his folly, the man walked forward towards the treasure. As soon as he moved closer, the tiger jumped upon him and killed him. He made a very tasty meal for the tiger indeed.

In this manner, the tiger tricked many foolish and greedy humans into becoming his meal, and he led a happy and fulfilled life for as long as he lived.

> Greed can prevent the mind
> from thinking clearly and prompt it
> to act foolishly.

The Grateful Tiger

O nce upon a time in a wild jungle, there lived a tiger. One day, as it was wandering around in the jungle, it stepped upon a thorn and injured itself.

The tiger tried very hard to rid itself off the thorn but was not successful. Defeated, it lay crying, howling loudly in one corner of the jungle.

A short while later a traveller crossed the jungle, to use a shortcut. He heard the howls and followed the sounds of pain. There, a short distance afar, he found the wounded tiger crying out in pain. The man was afraid of the tiger, but finally he took pity on the wounded animal, walked up to it, and pulled out the thorn. The tiger licked the man in gratitude and walked away, without harming him.

A few days later some dacoits invaded the jungle and took a few animals captive with them. The wounded tiger was also one of them. One day, the dacoits gathered some people from the village to play a cruel game. They wanted to see a man fight a beast, and threw a man into a gallows with the tiger in it.

The tiger, which had been starved for many days charged ahead, but stopped short of the man when it recognised, that he was the same person who had saved him from pain a few days ago.

The whole village watched spellbound as the mighty tiger lay curled like a gentle puppy at the foot of the terrified man. The man then remembered his own kind act and patted the tiger lovingly.

The dacoits were also moved by the unique sight, and let all the animals and men in their captivity free.

> One good turn, deserves another.
> Kindness transforms many-a-hearts.

The Kind Woodcutter

One upon a time in a jungle, a woodcutter was about to cut a large and beautiful tree. Just then, a beautiful form emerged from the tree. She smiled at the woodcutter and said, "Oh good man, I am the goddess of the jungle and I request you to not cut this tree."

The woodcutter was very surprised to see her and said, "But my dear lady, I sell fire wood and make money. If I do not cut the tree I won't make any money today, and my children will go hungry."

The goddess stopped to think and said. "You are right, but many families live in my tree. They will all suffer if you cut it. Why don't you collect the twigs and branches that have fallen and use them for a while? The next time you need wood, cut up an old tree that is almost dead. That way the families in this tree will not suffer."

The woodcutter agreed and left after collecting several shattered twigs, broken branches, and stray logs.

A few days later as the woodcutter was walking through the jungle again, he came face to face with a leopard. He did not know what to do. Just then a dove flew past the leopard and when the leopard turned to watch the bird a snake slithered up to it, and hissed wildly.

The leopard was petrified, and fled in the opposite direction, leaving the confused woodcutter behind. He asked the snake, "Are you going to bite me now?"

"No," said the snake. "I am here to help you, as also is the dove. You did not cut our tree when my babies were born, and I remember you telling the tree goddess that you had children. I did not want your children to be orphaned, so I did whatever I could, to save your life."

The woodcutter was touched. He thanked the snake and the dove and returned home without cutting any tree. He was sure if he chose a kind profession, he would always have the blessing and help of others.

Kindness is the world's greatest virtue.

The Hidden Treasure

Once upon a time, there lived a small community of merchants on the banks of the Arabian Sea. They were a prosperous community and earned most of their wealth through the trade of grains and fruits to nearby villages and small towns.

The people of the village always spoke of a hidden island in the middle of the sea that was very rich in

lost treasures, and other precious merchandise.

The younger generation always desired to set out on a brave journey to find the hidden island and the treasure that was buried there. But the elders always warned against it. "You never know what you may find. There must be a reason why the treasure was abandoned. We have enough. There's no need to go looking for a hidden treasure. In the hope of being pleasantly surprised, you might get rudely shocked.

But the young were enthusiastic and daring, and one day, without the permission of their elders, a group of four set out into the middle of the sea. The group comprised of Abdul, Ali, Nadeem and Irfan; four

friends who went everywhere together.

After sailing a short distance into the sea, Nadeem spotted a small boulder, on which some thing could be seen shining. Sure that this was the hidden treasure, he told his friends what he had seen and the group, rowed as fast as they could towards the spot.

Suddenly the boulder got bigger and revealed some more things like jewellery, unopened chests, broken boats, and other unidentified things. The four friends were very happy. They could not wait to collect the treasure and go back home. They were sure that they would receive a hero's welcome for taking back such a magnificent treasure.

But just then their boats rocked and Lo behold! Before them lay a large and ferocious looking giant whale! The treasure that they had seen was scattered on its broad back. Undoubtedly the group that had sailed before them had capsized on the whale, and the large mammal was using the treasure as bait to lure other unsuspecting travellers.

Ali remembered how the elders had warned them, and felt foolish about disobeying the intelligence and wisdom of the experienced folk of his village.

Alas! It was too late for realisation. When the friends realised their foolishness, their boats were too close to the giant creature and they too capsized and drowned.

Half knowledge is very dangerous.

The End